Kittens

by Bobby Lynn Maslen
pictures by John R. Maslen

Scholastic Inc.
New York • Toronto • London • Auckland • Sydney • Mexico City • New Delhi • Hong Kong • Buenos Aires

Available Bob Books®:

Set 1: Beginning Readers — With consistent new sounds added gradually, your new reader is gently introduced to all the letters of the alphabet. They can soon say, "I read the whole book!®"

Set 2: Advancing Beginners — The use of three-letter words and consistent vowel sounds in slightly longer stories build skill and confidence.

Set 3: Word Families — Consonant blends, endings and a few sight words advance reading skills while the use of word families keep reading manageable.

Set 4: Complex Words — Longer books and complex words engage young readers as proficiency advances.

Set 5: Long Vowels — Silent *e* and other vowel blends build young readers' vocabulary and aptitude.

Bob Books® Collections:

Collection 1 — Includes Set 1: Beginning Readers and part of Set 2: Advancing Beginners

Collection 2 — Includes part of Set 2: Advancing Beginners and Set 3: Word Families

Collection 3 — Includes Set 4: Complex Words and Set 5: Long Vowels

Ask for Bob Books at your local bookstore, or visit www.bobbooks.com.

ISBN 0-545-02693-8

Copyright © 1996 by Bobby Lynn Maslen. All rights reserved. Published by Scholastic Inc. by arrangement with Bob Books ® Publications LLC. SCHOLASTIC and associated logos are trademarks and/or registered trademarks of Scholastic Inc. BOB BOOKS is a registered trademark of Bob Books Publications LLC.

6 5 4 3 2   10 11/0

Printed in China   68
This edition first printing, September 2007

Jill met a big cat.

Jill was sad. Cat was sad.

"What is the matter?" said Jim.

"The cat had bad luck,"
said Jill.

"What?" said Jim.

"The cat has lost her kittens."

The cat and Jill and Jim are sad.

"Call the kittens," said Jim, but the kittens did not come.

Bill did come.
"I saw six kittens in my bed,"
said Bill.

Jill and Jim and Cat ran to Bill's bed.

The cat was happy.

"Purrr," said the kittens and Mama Cat.

The End

List of 40 words in <u>Kittens</u>

<u>Short Vowels</u>

<u>a</u>	<u>e</u>	<u>i</u>	<u>o</u>	<u>u</u>	<u>sight</u>	
sad	met	in	not	but	a	what
bad	bed	big	lost	luck	I	come
had	end	six			to	said
ran		did			my	purrr
and		Jim			the	Mama
has		Jill			was	is
cat		Bill			saw	
matter		kittens			are	
happy					call	
					her	

86 total words in *Kittens*